Tips for Reading Together

Children learn best when reading is fun.

- Talk about the title and the pictures on the cover.
- Discuss what you think the story might be about.
- Read the story together, inviting your child to read as much of it as they can.
- Give lots of praise as your child reads, and help them when necessary.
- Try different ways of helping if they get stuck on a word. For example, get them to say the first sound of the word, or break it into chunks, or read the whole sentence again, trying to guess the word. Focus on the meaning.
- Re-read the story later, encouraging your child to read as much of it as they can.

Children enjoy re-reading stories and this helps to build their confidence.

Have fun!

The Stolen Crown

Part I

Written by Roderick Hunt

Illustrated by Alex Brychta

OXFORD

UNIVERSITY PRESS

Read these words before you begin the story:

fallen

climb

castle

wonder

ruin

magnifying

wall

wonder

cushion

crown

valuable

guards

stolen

trouble

Can you think of a sentence with the word *valuable* in it?

The family went to see an old castle.
Most of it had fallen down a long time ago.
"It's just a ruin," said Chip.

Kipper wanted to climb on a wall, but
Dad said "no".

"We must look after old ruins," he said.

"Once upon a time, it was a big castle," said Biff. "I wonder what it was like to live here."

Mum found a good spot for a picnic.
Floppy saw a rabbit hole. He began to
dig in the ground.

Chip saw something shining in the
dirt, so he picked it up.

"It's a glass bead," he said.

"I wonder who lost it?" said Biff.

Chip looked at the bead through his magnifying glass. Then he put it in his pocket.

"I don't think it's valuable," he said.

Later, Chip came into Biff's room.
He had a book about castles.

Suddenly, the magic key began to
glow.

The magic took Biff and Chip back in
time. It took them to the castle.

Some people were waiting outside a
big door.

An important man came up.

"I am Lord Kent," said the man.

"Where is your present for the prince?"

Biff and Chip didn't have a present.
"Think of something, Chip," said Biff.
"Er ... we have a magic glass," said
Chip. "It makes small things look big."

"That is a good present," said Lord
Kent. "The prince will like it. Put it on
this cushion. Then wait outside in the
line."

At last, Biff and Chip went into a hall.
"That was quick thinking, Chip," said
Biff. "I wonder who this prince is."
"He must be important," said Chip.

The prince was sitting on a throne.
Chip gave him the magnifying glass.
"I love it!" said the prince.

The prince jumped off the throne and looked through the magnifying glass.

"Tomorrow is an important day," he said. "Tomorrow I will be the king."

"You can call me Henry, but tomorrow
I will be King Henry," he said. "Come
with me." He ran out of the hall.

Henry ran up some stairs.

"Come and see my crown," he said.
"I want to look at it through this magic
glass."

Two guards looked at Biff and Chip.
"We are here to see that the crown is
not stolen," said a soldier. "Hold your
arms up. We must search you."

Henry took Biff and Chip into a small
room in a tower. Biff and Chip gasped
when they saw the crown.

"It looks very valuable," said Chip.

"If it was stolen, I could not become king," said Henry. "But it is safe in this tower. Nobody could take it from here."

Henry took Biff and Chip to see his
horse.

"I shall ride him when I become king
tomorrow," he said.

Suddenly, they heard shouting.
Lord Kent ran up to Henry.

"Come quickly!" he shouted. "Your
crown has been stolen."

Henry ran back up the stairs to the
crown room. The guards were still
outside the door.

"The crown is missing," said a guard.

"How can it be missing?" asked Henry.

"We don't know," said a guard.

"Nobody has been here, except you."

"I know who stole it," said Lord Kent.

"These children have stolen it," Lord Kent went on. "They used magic to do it. Throw them in prison at once."

"Oh!" said Biff. "Now we're in trouble!"

Now read Part 2…

Think about the story

Word Search

l	h	e	l	c	u	m	v	b	a
i	e	h	i	f	r	t	e	d	p
b	l	e	g	c	k	o	s	a	x
d	m	d	u	p	u	n	w	v	k
f	e	u	a	m	p	s	o	n	r
z	t	h	r	o	n	e	r	a	t
k	h	s	d	p	c	f	d	i	o
a	m	l	s	r	n	o	w	e	w
i	k	j	u	i	y	g	u	a	e
n	c	u	s	h	i	o	n	s	r

Find these things from the castle in the word search:

helmet   sword   cushion   guards
crown   throne   tower

Useful common words repeated in this story and other books in the series:

what wanted family wonder something suddenly
important tomorrow gasped quickly trouble search
Names in the story: Chip Kipper Dad Biff Floppy Mum
Henry Lord Kent

More books for you to enjoy

Level 1:
Getting Ready

Level 2:
Atarting to Read

Level 3:
Becoming a Reader

Level 4:
Building Confidence

Level 5:
Reading with Confidence

OXFORD
UNIVERSITY PRESS

Great Clarendon Street,
Oxford OX2 6DP

Text © Roderick Hunt 2007
Illustrations © Alex Brychta 2007

First published 2007

This edition published 2110
All rights reserved

Read at Home Series Editors:
Kate Ruttle, Annemarie Young

British Library Cataloguing
in Publication Data available

ISBN: 9780198387787

10 9 8 7 6 5 4 3 2 1

Printed in China by Imago

Have more fun
with Read at Home